American Inside Out Evolution

Workbook | Intermediate | **B**

SUE KAY
VAUGHAN JONES
PHILIP KERR

macmillan education

Macmillan Education
Companies and representatives throughout the world
American Inside Out Evolution. Workbook Intermediate B

Adapted by Peter Magss and Catherine Smith / The Content Station team: Simon Campbell, George Wells, and Catherine Gray
Macmillan is a registered trademark.
First edition published 2017

ISBN: 978-607-473-628-1

Based on New American Inside Out Workbook Intermediate B

Editorial Manager: Patricia Muradas
Editorial Operations Coordinator: Veronica Teodorov Ferreira
Editor: Cintia Zaitune
Concept design: Martha Tadaieski
Page make-up: The Content Station
Illustrations: Karen Ahlschläger pp14
Graphic Production: Kelly Gobbo
Photographic research: The Content Station
Cover concept and design: Jean Aranha
Cover photo: Vitaliy Pozdeev | Dreamstime

The authors and publishers would like to thank the following for permission to reproduce their photographs:
Dreamstime / Phanuwatn p4, Dreamstime / Vincent Giordano p5, Dreamstime / Niroworld p8, Dreamstime / Krystal Slagle p9, Dreamstime / Rosshelen p11, Dreamstime / Louis Davilla Wiyono p12, Dreamstime / Sbukley p13, Dreamstime / Jaguarps p15, Dreamstime / Elena Kazanskaya p16(l), Dreamstime / Lineartestpilot p16(r), Dreamstime / Monkey Business Images p19, Dreamstime / Arne9001 p20, Dreamstime / Viktoria Shvydkova p21(l), Dreamstime / Zdravinjo p21(r), Dreamstime / Jemastock p22(l), Dreamstime / Sharplaninac p22 (c), Dreamstime / Mheim301165 p22(r), Dreamstime / Viorel Sima p25, Dreamstime / Chesterf p26, Dreamstime / Fashionstock.com p27.

CANIEM No. 2275

Macmillan Publishers S.A. de C.V.
Insurgentes Sur 1886
Col. Florida, CP 01030
Álvaro Obregón
Ciudad de México
Tel: +52 (55) 5482 2200
elt@grupomacmillan.com

www.grupomacmillan.com www.macmillan.com.mx www.macmillanenglish.com

Printed in Brazil

This book was printed in December, 2017 by: Eskenazi Indústria Gráfica Ltda, Avenida Miguel Frias Vasconcelos, 1023 - Jaguaré - São Paulo - SP.

Contents

7 News

GRAMMAR

1 **Underline the correct alternative.**

- a I don't mind **being / to be** the center of attention.
- b People tell **me / to me** that I'm perfect.
- c I want **having / to have** a pierced nose.
- d I can't stand **reading / to read** fashion magazines.
- e I enjoy **spending / to spend** money.
- f I need **getting / to get** a new camera.
- g I never ask people **helping / to help** me.
- h I've never tried **go / to go** on a diet.

Change the sentences to make them true for you.

2 **Rewrite the sentences beginning with the words given.**

- a "Don't touch it," he told me.
  He warned me not to touch it.
- b "I'll be there at eight," she said.
  She promised ______
- c "Why don't you sue the photographers?" he asked me.
  He suggested ______
- d "The interest rate changes from time to time," she told me.
  She explained ______
- e "I'd better not leave this job," I thought.
  I realized ______
- f "Forget about me," he said to his wife.
  He told ______
- g "OK, I'll see you both later," she said.
  She agreed ______
- h "Could you stop being mean?" he asked her.
  He asked ______

3 **Complete the questions with the words in the box.**

Are	be	been	being
Have	Is	~~was~~	were

- a When __was__ your house built?
- b Will your dinner ______ cooked for you this evening?
- c ______ you ever described as "glamorous"?
- d What was the last thing you ______ forced to do?
- e ______ you ever been told to go away?
- f ______ your private life talked about by other people?
- g Are you ______ watched by anyone right now?
- h Has your homework ______ checked recently?

Write true answers to the questions.

4 **Complete the sentences with the verb in parentheses in the passive form. Use the simple present, simple past, or present perfect.**

- a The rock star Sonia Thorne __was arrested__ at Los Angeles airport last night. (arrest)
- b She ______ after arriving on a flight from Miami. (stop)
- c Almost two kilos of cocaine ______ in her bags. (find)
- d This is the third time that Ms. Thorne ______ on drug charges. (arrest)
- e However, she ______. (never / convict)
- f Ms. Thorne ______ in a police station last night. (keep)
- g Because of her arrest, her concert at the Hollywood Bowl ______. (cancel)
- h It ______ that she will appear in court later today. (believe)

5 Rewrite the following sentences using a passive verb.

a The paparazzi followed the car for ten kilometers.
The car was followed by the paparazzi for ten kilometers.

b People photograph her when she walks down the street.
She ______________________

c The newspaper will pay her $50,000 for the pictures.
She ______________________

d They are going to put the pictures on the front page of the newspaper.
The pictures ______________________

e Thieves stole an enormous sum of money from a Hollywood celebrity last night.
Last night, an enormous sum of money ______________________

f Police officers have accused the football player Ed Flower of burglary.
The football player, Ed Flower, ______________________

6 Correct the following news stories by changing one verb in each story. Some need to be changed from active to passive, and some from passive to active.

a

> Donovan Thomas ~~was escaped~~ from prison in Rhode Island, in the USA, after serving 89 days of a 90-day sentence. He was caught and sentenced to an extra six months.

escaped

b

> Philip Johnson, 32, from Prestonburg, Kentucky, shot himself in the chest because he wanted to see if it hurt. He was discovered that it hurts a lot.

____

c

> *Circus girl, Jasmine Brown, 22, jailed for six days by a court in San Diego. She was riding an elephant on a busy highway and she was not wearing any clothes.*

____

d

> André Gurmon, from Montreal, Canada, was put an advertisement in the newspaper. It said: "Ladies—write to me if you are bored with the man in your life." He received a reply from his wife.

____

e

> Harrison Ford has several false teeth. Ford told the truth about his teeth after he voted sexiest man alive in a popular magazine.

____

f

> Hollywood star, Tom Duffy, has been seen with his new girlfriend, the glamorous Dolores Barker. The happy couple was being visited Trinidad for a short vacation.

____

VOCABULARY

1 Match the definitions with the words in the box.

desperate	hypocritical	insensitive
obsessed	~~photogenic~~	unflattering

a a person who looks good in pictures
photogenic

b believing something is so important that you think about it all the time
____

c making someone seem less pleasant or attractive than usual
____

d needing or wanting something very much
____

e not noticing or caring about the feelings or needs of other people
____

f saying that you believe certain things but behaving in a different way
____

2 Complete the sentences with words from Exercise 1.

a He was extremely insensitive and didn't listen to me at all.

b I'm ______________ to see her again.

c I'm the least ______________ person in the world and I don't have a single good picture of myself.

d Money, money, money, that's all she thinks about. She's completely ______________.

e Stop being so ______________. I know you don't really believe what you're saying.

f It's an interesting painting of her, but it's a little ______________.

3 **Match the TV shows with the descriptions.**

Tonight's top shows

Fugitives! (Channel 7, 7:00 p.m.-8.00 p.m.)
Parking Ticket (The Laugh Channel, 9:30 p.m.-10:15 p.m.)
Family Court (BBTV, 8:00 p.m.-9:00 p.m.)
Stop, Thief (TV22, 7:45 p.m.-8:30 p.m.)
Paparazzi Chase (Filmplus, 8:45 p.m.-10:30 p.m.)
Hot Gossip (BBTV, 11:00 p.m.-11:55 p.m.)

a Celebrities in the news – find out which Hollywood star is suspected of leading a double life.
Hot Gossip

b Comedy show about a glamorous officer in the highway patrol.
____

c Documentary about six convicted criminals who escaped from a high-security jail.
____

d Enjoyable action movie about a photographer who has to hide from a mysterious man in black.
____

e Ordinary members of the public in the fight against crime. This week: a burglar is caught in an embarrassing situation.
____

f Proceedings are dramatically stopped in Kate's divorce when the judge has a heart attack.
____

4 **Complete the sentences with the verbs in the box.**

~~arrested~~	committed	escaped
kidnapped	stolen	

a The police *arrested* her after a long car chase.
b She had ________ the car that she was driving.
c She had ________ more than fifty different crimes in twenty-four hours.
d In her worst crime, she had ________ a ten-year-old child.
e She ________ after only two weeks by climbing over a wall.

5 **Complete the email with the words in the box.**

Actually	Anyway	~~great~~	Guess	let
Love	news	Talking	thing	touch

Dear Pia,
It was (1) *great* to hear from you. I didn't know the (2) ________ about Anna and Giorgio, but I'm not sorry to hear it. They weren't getting along at all.
(3) ________, I never liked Giorgio, and Anna deserves someone better than him. The good (4) ________ now is that she can look for someone else.
I heard from Sue, who was in (5) ________ last week. She's looking forward to her baby and she's had all the tests. Apparently, it's a boy, so her husband is happy, but I think she wanted a girl.
(6) ________ of happy couples, it sounds as though you're very happy with your new boss!
(7) ________, I was so happy to hear that you're taking a vacation in August. (8) ________ what? I'm on vacation then, too. I'll (9) ________ you know my exact dates when I have them. Why don't we do something together?
(10) ________,
Ian

6 **Number the lines in the correct order to make a mini-conversation.**

Conversation 1
a ☐ I was arrested last night.
b ☐ Oh, no. I'm sorry to hear that. What happened?
c ☐ That's terrible. Who did they think you were?
d ☐ The police thought I was someone else.
e ☐ You don't look too happy. How are things going?

Conversation 2
a ☐ Mine, actually.
b ☐ Yes, I'm going to an engagement party.
c ☐ Are you doing anything interesting this weekend?
d ☐ Lucky you! Whose is it?

Conversation 3
a ☐ Guess what?
b ☐ How annoying!
c ☐ I got a parking ticket this afternoon.
d ☐ What?

032 **Listen and check.**

PRONUNCIATION

1 033 **Listen and repeat the sentences. Notice the way that some words are joined together.**
a Kate Moss asked‿us‿not‿to take pictures‿of‿her daughter.
b People also want‿to‿think that they're just‿normal people.
c She stopped‿to ask‿her‿if she was‿OK.
d They want to know what he's going‿to do‿about‿it.

2 034 **Listen and figure out the correct spelling of the following phrases.**
a wannathink
want to think
b promistachange
____
c forgeddaboudit
____

d jusdoingajob

____

e wotchagonnadoaboudit

____

f wazityafirstime

____

WRITING

Writing an essay

Linking sentences with *although*, *despite*, *however*

1 Read the examples in the box, showing how to contrast ideas using *although*, *despite*, and *however*.

Contrasting ideas

although

Although I'm a fan of Alicia Keys, I'm not interested in her private life.

He claims his marriage is happy, although he was seen at a New York club with his personal assistant.

despite

Despite the fact that I'm a fan of Alicia Keys, I'm not interested in her private life.

He claims his marriage is happy, despite the fact that he was seen in a New York club with his personal assistant.

however

I'm a fan of Alicia Keys. However, I'm not interested in her private life.

He claims his marriage is happy. However, he was seen at a New York club with his personal assistant.

2 Complete the sentences with *although*, *despite*, or *however*.

a A lot of people buy gossip magazines, *despite* the fact that they contain a lot of trash.

b Young people often look up to movie and rock stars. ______________, these celebrities are not always good role models.

c ______________ some celebrities say they hate the tabloid press, they sometimes sell their stories to these newspapers for a lot of money.

d ______________ I like some movie stars, I'm not interested in reading about their love lives.

e Most people like to read gossip, ______________ the fact that they claim the opposite.

f Newspapers should not be allowed to print lies. ______________, it's important for the press to remain free.

3 Complete the sentences with the words in the box.

believe	conclusion	considered	more
~~opinion~~	point	remember	wrong

a In my *opinion*, it is wrong for the press to photograph the private lives of movie stars.

b Personally, I ______________ that we have the right to know about their lives.

c However, it is important to ______________ that the press sometimes goes too far.

d Although some people feel that it is ______________ to print these stories, many stars do not mind at all.

e However, perhaps the most important ______________ is what the individual celebrities think about it.

f What is ______________, some celebrities will sell their stories to the press.

g All things ______________, I do not think that we should ban this kind of reporting.

h In ______________, I would say that we should ban the reporting of these scandals.

4 Write an essay, using the title and essay plan below.

a First, make a plan on a piece of paper. Use some of the ideas from Exercise 2 to help you.

b Before you start, look at the language in Exercise 3 to help you.

Celebrity scandals* in the press: should they be banned?

Paragraph 1: Introduction
Explain that some people think that the reporting of celebrity scandals in the press should be banned. You might want to give an example of such a scandal.

Paragraph 2: Give your opinion and choose at least two reasons for this. Also give arguments against your reasons.

Paragraph 3: State the opposite opinion with at least two reasons that could be given for it. Argue against these reasons.

Paragraph 4: Conclusion
Give your opinion again.

*scandals = reports in the press about shocking behavior

8 Travel

GRAMMAR

1 **Can you name the countries: A, B, and C? Choose from this list:**

Angola
Brazil
Colombia
Cuba
Honduras
Mozambique
Uruguay
Venezuela

Country	A	B	C
Population	about 32 million	about 208 million	about 11 million
Official language	Spanish	Portuguese	Spanish
Climate	tropical	tropical and sub-tropical	semi-tropical
Main exports	oil, aluminum	iron, steel, soybean, machinery, coffee	sugar, tobacco, coffee
Highest mountain	4,979 m	2,993 m	1,974 m

2 **Look at the table above again and complete the sentences with the words in the box.**

Country A

~~couldn't~~	definitely	guess	might

a It _couldn't_ be Brazil, because they speak Portuguese in Brazil.

b I think it ___________ be Colombia, because there are some high mountains there, aren't there?

c I ___________ it could be Venezuela. I think they have lots of oil.

d It ___________ isn't Uruguay, because I'm sure that it isn't tropical.

Country B

couldn't	certainly	could	must

a It's ___________ not Cuba, because that's Spanish-speaking.

b And it ___________ be Honduras – that's not a very industrialized country.

c It ___________ be Angola – I think they have a climate like that.

d It ___________ be Brazil. None of the other countries have so many people.

Now write similar sentences about Country C.

a ______________________________

b ______________________________

c ______________________________

d ______________________________

3 **Read the text and number the sentences below in the order in which they happened in Michael Crichton's life.**

Michael Crichton, the author of *Jurassic Park*, was one of the world's greatest travelers. In his autobiography, *Travels*, he describes how he began "serious" traveling when he was 30 and he went to Bangkok. He then began his amazing adventures, which included diving with sharks off Tahiti, watching gorillas in the Congo, and living in the jungle in New Guinea.

It all began in Los Angeles, where Crichton was writing movies for Hollywood. He had given up his studies at Harvard Medical School and he had separated from his wife, because he wanted to spend his time writing. At Harvard, he had already sold one movie, *The Andromeda Strain*, to Hollywood, and he had begun to lose interest in medicine.

In LA, he made the successful science-fiction movie *Westworld*, but he then fell into a depression and did not know what to do next. He decided to go to Bangkok, because a friend of his who lived there had invited him. It was the beginning of an incredible life of traveling.

a A friend invited him to Bangkok. ______

b He fell into a depression. ______

c He left Harvard. ______

d He made *Westworld*. ______

e He sold *The Andromeda Strain* to Hollywood. __1__

f He went to Bangkok. ______

g He went to Los Angeles. ______

h He went to Tahiti and the Congo. ______

4 **Put the verbs in parentheses into the simple past or the past perfect.**

a Before he left Harvard, Michael Crichton _had already sold_ (already / sell) a movie to Hollywood.

b He wanted to leave Harvard because he ______________ (think) the classes were boring.

c He separated from his wife before he ________ (go) to LA.

d He went to Los Angeles because he ________ (decide) to spend his time writing.

e After he went to Los Angeles, he ________ (fall) into a depression.

f He remembered that a friend ________ (invite) him to Thailand.

g When he arrived in Bangkok, his friend ________ (meet) him at the airport.

h Before he went to Bangkok, he ________ (never / be) outside America or Europe.

5 Write three true sentences about the topics below.

- three things that you had done before ten o'clock this morning
- three things you had eaten or drunk before lunchtime yesterday
- three people you had spoken to today before you began this exercise

VOCABULARY

1 Complete the sentences with the words in the box.

between	far	~~in~~	in	not
of	of	on	on	to

a I live (1) __in__ the north-west (2) ________ my country not (3) ________ from the mountains. My village is (4) ________ the north of Chiang Mai, which is the nearest big city.

b I live in the south-west of the country. The town is (5) ________ the coast, but we're (6) ________ far from the mountains.

c I live (7) ________ the north of the country. The town is (8) ________ a lake to the north of Milan.

d I live on an island in Lake Titicaca (9) ________ the mountains (10) ________ Peru and Bolivia.

Which place (a, b, c, or d) is shown in the picture?

2 Complete the sentences with the words in the box.

ancient	~~Buddhist~~	high-rise
skyline	snow-capped	waterfall

a There are seven temples at the __Buddhist__ monastery of Taktshang, Bhutan, which hangs from a cliff at 700 meters above the river below.

b There are many good ski resorts in the ________ Rocky Mountains.

c The ________ ruins of Stonehenge were possibly a temple to a sun god.

d Water from the Tortum Lake, 100 kilometers north of Erzurum in eastern Turkey, falls 48 meters in a spectacular ________ into the river below.

e You can get a good view of the Manhattan ________ from the Statue of Liberty.

f You can go to the roof of many of the ________ buildings in Manhattan.

3 Underline the correct alternative below to complete the texts.

The Yucatán Peninsula

Most of the beaches are (1) by apartment buildings and restaurants. They are especially (2) with tourists and the beautiful sands are full of (3). But there are still some (4) places. The prettiest part of the coast is Puerto Morelos, where you get spectacular (5) of the ocean.

The Sussex Coast

The towering white (6) of Sussex in the (7) part of England begin at the headland of Beachy Head. You can follow the coastal path all the way to Brighton. In Brighton, there are some great stores and cute little pubs on (8) streets. The Grand Hotel, (9) the beach, is a great place for afternoon tea.

1 **packed / popular / surrounded**
2 **hidden / overlooking / popular**
3 **beach communities / lounge chairs / white sands**
4 **local / sandy / unspoiled**
5 **coves / lagoons / views**
6 **bay / beaches / cliffs**
7 **island / southern / watersports**
8 **coral / hidden / overlooking**
9 **dynamite / overlooking / ranging**

4 **Complete the sentences with the words in the box.**

all or nothing	come and go	give or take
neat and tidy	~~peace and quiet~~	sooner or later
	take it or leave it	

a I like to work very early in the morning, when I can have some _peace and quiet_.

b I don't mind tea, but I can ________________.

c I always keep my desk ________________.

d My English class lasts an hour, ________________ ________ a few minutes.

e When I meet someone new, I either like them or I can't stand them – it's ________________.

f During our English classes, we can ____________ ________ as we please.

g I have exams at the end of the year and ____________ I'll need to start some serious studying.

Check (✓) the sentences that are true for you.

5 **Match the directions (a, b, and c) from City Hall (*A*) to three different subway stations (1, 2, 3 or 4).**

a Go out of City Hall and take a right. Go to the end of the street, take a right again, and then take the third street on your left. You'll see a subway station at the end of the street.
Subway station ________

b Go out of City Hall and take a right. At the end of the street, take a left and then take the first street on your right. Go straight until you get to the end. Take a right and you'll see a subway station on the other side of the street.
Subway station ________

c Go out of City Hall and take a left. Follow the street to the end and then take a right. After that, I think it's the first street on the right again, and you go on until you see the subway station in front of you.
Subway station ________

6 **Write directions from City Hall (A) to a restaurant (B).**

a ________________________________

b ________________________________

c ________________________________

d ________________________________

e ________________________________

f ________________________________

PRONUNCIATION

1 **Write the missing letters to complete the words. The words in each group have the same vowel sound.**

a /ɔ/

a	al	~~au~~	aw

<u>au</u>thor f _ _ l s _ _ w _ ter

b /ɜr/

er	ir	or	ur

p _ _ son c _ _ ving w _ _ st f _ _ st

c /ɑr/

ar	ear

h _ _ _ t g _ _ den _ _ m m _ _ ket

035 **Listen and repeat.**

2 **Put the words in the box into three groups according to the vowel sound.**

~~all~~	ball	~~birds~~	bought
~~car~~	girl	hardly	large
part	return	start	surf
wall	water	world	

/ɔ/	/ɜr/	/ɑr/
all	birds	car

036 **Listen and check. Repeat the words.**

LISTENING

1 037 **Cover the listening script and listen to six people talking about their vacations. Decide if they enjoyed their vacation or not. Put ☺ or ☹ in the box.**

1	2	3	4	5	6

2 **Listen again and match a topic from the box to each of the speakers.**

Topic	Speaker
entertainment	
food	
hotel	
trip	
money and prices	
weather	

3 **Listen again. Are the statements true (T) or false (F)?**

Speaker 1

a They didn't like the restaurants or excursions. ______

b They didn't have enough money. ______

Speaker 2

c The vacation was very tiring. ______

d They sometimes slept during the day. ______

Speaker 3

e The hotel was not very clean. ______

f The hotel staff was very friendly. ______

Speaker 4

g The plane was only a little late. ______

h They missed the train. ______

Speaker 5

i They didn't enjoy their first meal. ______

j The restaurants in the town were very good. ______

Speaker 6

k They were unhappy about the snow. ______

l The weather had been better the previous year. ______

1 The resort was great with a beautiful sandy beach. The problem was that everything cost a fortune. Fantastic restaurants, amazing excursions, windsurfing, diving, they had everything, but basically we did nothing at all because we couldn't afford it. After two days, we had spent all our money, so we just ate sandwiches after that, and watched everyone else enjoying themselves.

2 I was dead by the end of it. I've always wanted to go, so I decided to really enjoy myself. We didn't do much during the day because we needed our sleep, but in the evenings we saw a musical and then went dancing at a different place every night. Awesome! I can't wait to get back!

3 Yes, fantastic. The hotel was an ugly high-rise building – they hadn't even finished building it. It was absolutely filthy, and there didn't seem to be anyone working there. Oh yes, there was a man at reception, but he was asleep most of the time. It was the perfect destination for your worst enemy.

4 When we got to the check-in they said there was a short delay. Six hours later, we finally got on to an ancient plane, and when we were airborne, I just closed my eyes and hoped. When we arrived, we were too late for the train and, in any case, they had lost our baggage somewhere.

5 On the first day, we went down to the hotel restaurant and it was awful. They served us some kind of fish head in a spicy sauce. Ugh! So for the rest of the time we decided to go downtown where there were restaurants on every corner. We found some really amazing places and we couldn't wait for dinner time to arrive.

6 The funny thing is that although it was very cold, I actually got a little bit of sunburn. There had been a lot of snow just before we got there, so conditions were perfect. The resort was really at its best. It's a shame it wasn't like that last year.

9 Opinions

GRAMMAR

1 **Write true sentences for you using the verbs *tell* and *say*.**

2 **Put the movie quotes into reported speech and remember that the tenses move back. You will need to change some of the pronouns.**

a "Life is like a box of chocolates." (*Forrest Gump*)
His mother said that life was like a box of chocolates.

b "I'm coming for you." (*A Nightmare on Elm Street*)
Freddy told the children

c "You broke my heart, Fredo." (*The Godfather II*)
He told Fredo

d "His eyes have made love to me all evening." (*Camille*)
She said

e "I'll be back." (*The Terminator*)
He said

f "I'm going to make him an offer he can't refuse." (*The Godfather*)
He said

g "I had a farm in Africa." (*Out of Africa*)
She said

h "We'll always have Paris." (*Casablanca*)
Her told her

3 **Rewrite the text in direct speech.**

She told me that her favorite movie was *Titanic*. She explained that she had already seen it six times and that she was going to watch it again tonight. She said that she was a great fan of Kate Winslet and that she was hoping to meet her one day. She said that she particularly liked the ending, although it always made her cry. She said that she didn't find Leonardo DiCaprio very attractive, but she thought he was a great actor.

My favorite movie is Titanic. I ...

038 **Listen and check.**

4 **Correct the grammatical mistakes in four of the sentences below. Check (✓) the correct sentences.**

a She asked me who my favorite living author was.
✓

b She asked me what was the title of his last book.

c She asked me how many books he had written.

d She asked me which book had I read first.

e She asked me I was going to read any of his books again.

f She asked me whether I had read all his books.

g She asked me did I know anything about his life.

h She asked me what I was reading now.

Put the questions into direct speech.

a

b

c

d

e

f

g

h

5 **Put the questions into reported speech, moving the tenses back.**

a Did you enjoy it?
She asked me ___if I had enjoyed it.___

b Who are the main characters?
She asked me ____________________

c How does the story begin?
She asked me ____________________

d Would you like to read it again?
She asked me ____________________

e What will you read next?
She asked me ____________________

f Did anyone recommend the book to you?
She asked me ____________________

g Was it easy to get into?
She asked me ____________________

h Do you ever stop reading a book before the end?
She asked me ____________________

VOCABULARY

1 **Underline the correct alternative.**

a The black and white **photography** / **premiere** was especially beautiful.

b The movie has a very happy **ending** / **hit**.

c It was a real **musical** / **tearjerker** and everybody was crying.

d I had to read the **fantasy** / **subtitles** because I couldn't understand what they were saying.

e The **plot** / **soundtrack** included two excellent songs by Elton John.

f The movie was **based on** / **set in** New York in the twenty-third century.

g I'm not sure whether it's a horror movie or a **storyline** / **thriller** – both, I guess.

2 **Match the movie titles (a–h) with the types of movies (1–8).**

a *The First Kiss*
b *Cut, Burn, Kill*
c *Al Capone and the Chicago Mafia*
d *My Girlfriend's Sense of Humor*
e *Mysterious Planet*
f *The Confident Cowboy*
g *They Died for their Country*
h *CIA: Secret Agent*

1 gangster movie
2 horror movie
3 love story
4 romantic comedy
5 science-fiction movie
6 spy movie
7 war movie
8 western

a	b	c	d	e	f	g	h
3							

3 **Write the missing letters.**

a My favorite (1) alb _u_ _m_ is called *Live at the Roxy* and my favorite song is the eighth (2) tra _ _, *No Woman, No Cry*. It's a recording of the great (3) regg _ _ singer, Bob Marley, performing (4) li _ _ at a (5) g _ _ in West Hollywood in 1976. I know the (6) lyr _ _ _ to all his songs and I love singing them. I play them at full volume on my (7) spea _ _ _ _ at home and annoy the neighbors.

b I can't stand modern music like (1) tec _ _ _ or (2) hip- _ _ _. I prefer (3) class _ _ _ _ music, like Beethoven or Mozart. I especially enjoy going to the (4) ope _ _. I play the violin in an (5) orche _ _ _ _ in my town and I also play in a folk (6) ba _ _. We do a lot of traditional (7) dan _ _ music.

4 **Complete the text with the words in the box.**

chapters	character	cover	ending	get
gripping	~~novel~~	paperback	plot	put

The last (1) ___novel___ I read was called *The Girl on the Train*. The reviews all said it was (2) ____________ and that you couldn't (3) ____________ it down after you'd started reading it. But after about four (4) ____________, I was still finding it hard to (5) ____________ into. The main (6) ____________ is Rachel Watson, a 32-year-old alcoholic who is obsessed with a couple she watches from the train every day. She often has blackouts and can't remember anything when she wakes up. The (7) ____________ gets complicated when one of the characters is murdered. The best part of the story is the (8) ____________, when the murderer is revealed. The (9) ____________ of the (10) ____________ edition of the book shows a picture from the movie that is based on the book. In the movie, Rachel Watson is played by actress Emily Blunt.

5 **Complete the adjectives with *ing* or *ed*.**

a He's so annoy_ing_ – I really don't like him at all.
b I was so bor_____ I almost fell asleep.
c You may find this quite challeng_____, but tell me if you have a problem.
d She was a little confus_____ after his terrible explanation.
e He was very disappoint_____ with his performance when he learned that he hadn't won.
f It's one of the most excit_____ movies I've ever seen.
g Her autobiography was absolutely fascinat_____ and I couldn't put it down.
h I usually feel more relax_____ after a cup of hot chocolate.
i It's such an amazing story that I felt really inspir_____ after reading it.

6 **Complete the conversations with the phrases (a–h).**

a As far as I'm concerned
b do you know what I think
c do you think
d Don't you think
e I agree
f I'm not so sure
g see your point
h that's true, but

A: (1) __d__ that's absolutely fantastic?
B: Definitely. (2) ______, he's the best artist in the world today.
A: Yes, (3) ______ with you. In fact, if you ask me, he's the best artist in the world ever!
B: Yes, probably. I think this is definitely his best painting.
A: Oh, (4) ______ about that. He's done so many great paintings.
C: What (5) ______ of that picture?
D: It's awful. In fact, (6) ______? A baby could paint better than that.
C: Yes, (7) ______ a baby might choose more attractive colors.
D: Yes, I (8) ______.

039 **Listen and check.**

PRONUNCIATION

1 040 **Listen and check (✓) the words that you hear.**

a day — die ✓
b fail — file
c late — light
d main — mine
e tape — type
f wait — white

2 **Put the words in the box in the correct column according to the vowel sound.**

~~age~~	~~buy~~	change	child	claim	cry
date	great	guy	mind	night	quite
save	strange	way	wild		

/eɪ/	/aɪ/
age	buy

041 **Listen and check. Repeat the words.**

WRITING

Writing a movie review
Making generalizations

1 **Read the movie review and check (✓) the topics that are mentioned.**

- the cast ✓
- the ending ☐
- the plot ☐
- the script ☐
- the soundtrack ☐
- the special effects ☐

Movie Review

Guardians of the Galaxy is a science-fiction superhero movie that was a big hit in 2014. It was co-written and directed by James Gunn. *Guardians of the Galaxy* is based on the characters in a series of Marvel comic books. It stars Chris Pratt, Zoe Saldana, Dave Bautista and Vin Diesel and there are many other well-known actors, too.

The movie tells the story of Peter Quill, who is kidnapped by space pirates as a child. 26 years later, Peter organizes a group of criminals to save the galaxy from the evil Ronan. Set in a fantasy universe, the plot is not always easy to understand, but on the whole the details of the story are not terribly important.

The script is very funny and the acting is generally excellent. Chris Pratt, who plays Peter Quill, brings plenty of energy to the many fight scenes in the movie. I was especially impressed by the soundtrack. It includes twelve songs from the 70s and 80s and even topped the US charts for a few weeks.

Guardians of the Galaxy is full of action and it's funny at the same time. As a piece of Hollywood entertainment, I thoroughly recommend it.

2 **Find phrases in the review that you can replace with the phrases below.**

a I particularly liked
b it is certainly worth seeing
c The movie is about
d Taking place in
e The starring roles are taken by
f the story is hard to follow
g very popular with movie-goers

3 **Look at the examples in the box. Then choose the best way to complete the sentences about a movie you know.**

> **Making generalizations**
>
> *On the whole,* / *In general,* / *By and large,* — the acting is excellent
>
> The acting is *generally* excellent.

a On the whole, the plot is **a little confusing** / **not terribly believable** / **very engaging**.
b In general, the main characters of the movie are **a little disappointing** / **very convincing** / **very interesting**.
c By and large, the action scenes are **boring** / **thrilling** / **very well done**.
d The movie's soundtrack is generally **just right** / **quite inspiring** / **very annoying**.

4 **Write a review of a movie that you have seen. Use the paragraph plan below to help you.**

Paragraph 1
- What is the movie title?
- What kind of movie is it?
- When was it made?
- Who stars in it?
- Who directed it?
- How successful or popular was it?

Paragraph 2
- Where is it set?
- Who are the main characters?
- What happens in the movie? (Use the simple present to tell the story of the movie.)

Paragraph 3
- What did you like or dislike about the movie?
- What were the acting, the script, the soundtrack, etc. like?
- Were some parts of the movie better or worse than others?

Paragraph 4
- On the whole, did you enjoy the movie?
- Would you recommend it to other people?
- Why or why not?

10 Childhood

GRAMMAR

1 Delete the relative pronoun that is not possible.

a ... a sister **that / ~~which~~ / who** doesn't pull my hair!
b ... a house **that / which / who** has a big backyard.
c ... a school **that / which / who** I like.
d ... a teacher **that / which / who** doesn't give much homework.
e ... a friend **that / which / who** will let me win our games.
f ... a lot of cousins **that / which / who** are the same age as me.
g ... hair **that / which / who** is dark and curly.

2 Join the pairs of sentences with a relative clause.

a My dad is a nice guy. He gives me lots of presents.
My dad is a nice guy who gives me lots of presents.

b Dad lives with a new girlfriend. She doesn't like me.
____
____

c She has a daughter. I sometimes play with her.
____
____

d They have a house by the ocean. I really like it.
____
____

e My mom and I have a small apartment. She's really proud of it.
____
____

f Mom has a job. It's not very well paid.
____
____

g She works for a man. He looks like my father.
____
____

h This is a picture of my dad. I drew it.
____
____

3 Choose the most logical way to complete the sentences with *if* or *unless*.

a You'll never find a good job *unless* you go to college.
b Children are often unhappy __________ they have pushy parents.
c Children are much happier __________ they are brought up in the countryside.
d __________ you want your children to be successful, they have to learn English.
e You shouldn't have children __________ you have a lot of money.
f Life is very hard __________ you come from a rich family.
g Children never learn __________ you yell at them from time to time.

Check (✓) the sentences that you agree with.

4 Rewrite the sentences in Exercise 3 that contain *unless*. Replace *unless* with *if* and make any other necessary changes.

You'll never find a good job if you don't go to college.
____
____
____
____
____

5 Correct the mistake in each sentence.

a Do you know why ~~did Hayley run~~ *Hayley ran* away from home?

b Can you tell me this was the first time?

c Do you think if she's been sick recently?

d Could you tell me if does she have a boyfriend?

e Do you know where she did go?

f Do you think that she having problems at school?

g Do you have any idea will she do it again?

6 Change the direct questions into indirect questions.

a Do children have too much freedom?
Do you think *children have too much freedom?*

b Where is your son now?
Do you have any idea ______

c Is your child under stress at school?
Can you tell me ______

d What do your children think of you?
Could you tell me ______

e Are your children happy?
Do you know ______

f Is school more important than the family in a child's education?
Do you think ______

VOCABULARY

1 Complete the phrasal verbs with a preposition.

a I remember that my neighbors used to yell *at* me every time I kicked my ball into their backyard.

b I didn't mind helping with the cooking, but I hated cleaning ______.

c I was a very independent child and my parents knew that there was no need to worry ______ me.

d I wasn't a very good child and my parents were always telling me ______ for something or other.

e When I came home late, my parents sat ______ waiting for me.

f On Saturday evenings, a babysitter came to take care ______ me when my parents were out.

g When my parents came to tuck me ______, they always gave me a big kiss.

h My parents died when I was in my teens and I was brought ______ by my grandparents.

2 Match the dictionary definitions with the phrasal verbs in Exercise 1.

1 care for someone or something and make certain that they have everything they need; 2 be responsible for something

a *take care of*

1 [often passive] Take care of a child until he or she becomes an adult; 1a teach a child to behave in a particular way or to have particular beliefs; 1b used for saying where or how someone lived when they were a child

b ______

informal criticize someone for doing something wrong

c ______

feel nervous and upset because you keep thinking about a problem that you have or could have in the future

d ______

to go to bed later than usual

e ______

put a child into bed and make sure that they are warm and comfortable by covering them well

f ______

say something to someone in a loud voice, usually because you are angry

g ______

make a place look better by putting things in the correct place

h ______

3 **Put the words in order to complete the questions.**
When you were 13 years old, ...

a did do make parents the dishes you your ?
did your parents make you do the dishes?

b a did have let cell phone they you ?
____

c did dinner eat front in let of the they TV you ?
____

d did make they room clean up you your ?
____

e horror did movies let they you watch ?
____

f a at did friend's house let sleep they you?
____

Write true answers to the questions.

____
____
____
____
____
____

4 **Rewrite the sentences using *make* or *let*.**

a My parents forced me to go to church every Sunday.
My parents *made me go to church every Sunday.*

b The boss never allows us to take a day off.
The boss ______________________

c I don't allow the dog to come into the house.
I ______________________

d You're going to force me to get angry.
You're ______________________

e They didn't allow us to have any freedom.
They ______________________

f Will you allow me to come with you?
Will you ______________________

g Don't force her to talk if she doesn't want to.
Don't ______________________

5 **Complete the sentences with the words in the box.**

~~for~~	like	looks	
of	thing	use	with

Chopsticks fan

A: Have you seen this? It's a chopsticks fan.
B: A what? What's it (1) *for*?
A: It's a fan that you attach to your chopsticks and you (2) ______ it to cool down your food while you're eating.

Butter stick

A: Could you pass me the butter stick, please?
B: The butter stick? What does it look (3) ______?
A: It's that thing over there that (4) ______ like a lipstick or a tube of glue. It's for putting butter on your bread.

Banana holder

A: Excuse me. Do you sell banana holders?
B: Banana holders? I'm sorry, what do you do (5) ______ them?
A: You put a banana in them. It's the same shape as a banana. It's made (6) ______ plastic and it's a (7) ______ you use to protect your bananas.

PRONUNCIATION

1 **Look at the underlined vowel sounds. Circle the word which has a different sound.**

a	about	allow	doubt	down	own
b	annoyed	choice	employ	going	join
c	clothes	cope	drove	ghost	love

042 **Listen and check.**

2 **Put the words in the box in the correct column according to the vowel sound.**

~~enjoy~~	~~found~~	~~grow~~	hole	how
know	noise	our	own	point
proud	round	toilet	toy	won't

/ɔɪ/	/aʊ/	/oʊ/
enjoy	*found*	*grow*

043 **Listen and check. Repeat the words.**

LISTENING

1 ▶ 044 **Cover the listening script and listen to the teacher's story. Number the events (a–h) in the order in which they happened.**

a A girl started crying. ______
b The teacher went to look for the girls. ______
c The principal spoke to Mr. Burr. ______
d A girl left the room. ______
e The teacher realized why the girls had really left the room. ______
f The students began a test. __1__
g The teacher returned to the classroom. ______
h The girl's friend went to help her. ______

2 **Look at the script and find expressions which mean the same as the following:**

a I had no idea (*paragraph 1*)
____
b make your life difficult (*paragraph 2*)
____
c I was responsible (*paragraph 2*)
____
d she still hadn't come back (*paragraph 4*)
____
e the only thing to do was (*paragraph 4*)
____
f very well behaved (*paragraph 5*)
____

3 **Find four places in the first paragraph where you can add *that*. The first one has been done for you.**

John Burr, a teacher who works in a Chicago school, was asked about his worst teaching experience.

I think that the worst experience ^that I've ever had was in my first year of teaching, and the kids knew that I didn't have a clue how to control them. I was giving the students a French test, a subject most of them hated. I had a class of eighth graders and these children do anything they can to give you a hard time. It's the age group I find the most difficult.

There was one girl in the class whose mother had died recently. She used to sit there and stare at me, as if it was my fault. And she had a friend who sat next to her, who was probably the biggest trouble-maker in the whole school.

Anyway, one day, the students were taking their test – it was about relative clauses, which we'd just done in class – when this girl started crying. She put up her hand and asked if she could go to the bathroom. I knew that she was probably thinking about her mother, so I said yes. I mean, what else could I do? So she left the room and ten minutes later she still hadn't come back. I was wondering what to do next when her friend put up her hand and asked if she could go and look for her. I couldn't go myself because the students would all cheat, so I said yes, and she left the room, too.

Ten minutes later, there was still no sign of her. I thought there was nothing for me to do but to go and find them both myself. I was coming out of the girls' bathroom – they weren't there – when the principal called me from the other end of the corridor. "Mr. Burr!" he yelled. "Is there any particular reason why your students are all talking to each other in the middle of a test? I suggest that you get back to your classroom immediately."

I ran back to my classroom and there were the two girls, sitting quietly, as good as gold. The rest of the class was also quiet, continuing with their test. It was only when I graded the test that I understood what had happened. The whole class scored more than 80% – the first and last time that ever happened!

11 Age

GRAMMAR

1 **Write the words in the correct order to make sentences.**

a wish hadn't smoking I started I .

____

b could vacation If go only on I .

____

c told only I had truth the her If .

____

d didn't so homework much I wish have I .

____

e I swim had I to learned wish .

____

f wasn't it wish I raining .

____

2 **Write a wish or regret for the sentences below.**

a I have so many regrets.
I wish *I didn't have so many regrets.*

b I don't have a lot of money.
I wish ______________________________

c I can never find time to read.
I wish ______________________________

d I didn't pay attention in class yesterday.
I wish ______________________________

e I overslept this morning.
I wish ______________________________

f I ate too much for dinner last night.
I wish ______________________________

g I'm not good at sports.
I wish ______________________________

h I feel anxious all the time.
I wish ______________________________

Check (✓) the wishes or regrets that are true for you.

3 **Put the verbs in parentheses into the appropriate tense.**

a Where *would you live* (you live) if you could live anywhere in the world?

b If you ______________ (not need) to work, what would you do with your life?

c If you could change one thing about your appearance, what ______________ (you change)?

d What ______________ (you say) if you met your favorite movie star?

e If you ______________ (be) invited to a party in Hollywood, what would you wear?

f How would you feel if the government in your country ______________ (change)?

g What would you do if you only ______________ (have) twenty-four hours to live?

h If you had three wishes, what ______________ (they be)?

Write true answers to the questions.

a ______________________________
b ______________________________
c ______________________________
d ______________________________
e ______________________________
f ______________________________
g ______________________________
h ______________________________

4 **Write unreal conditional sentences based on the situations below.**

a I don't understand. I can't explain.
If I understood, I would / I'd be able to explain.

b I feel tired. I won't go out tonight.

____

c I'm in love. I think about him all the time.

____

d I'm not a liar. I tell the truth.

____

e I can't dance. I don't go to nightclubs.

____

f I love Coldplay. I buy all their albums.

____

g I have five children. I spend a lot of time cooking.

____

5 **Put the verbs in parentheses into the correct tense.**

a If I had met the right person, I *would have gotten* (get) married.

b If I ________________ (go) out more often, I would have met more people.

c I ________________ (go) out more often if I had had more time.

d I would have had more time if I ________________ (not work) so hard.

e I ________________ (not work) so hard if I hadn't needed the money.

f If I had had more money, I ________________ (be) more relaxed.

g I ________________ (have) more friends if I had been more relaxed.

6 **Complete the sentences so that they are true for you.**

a If I had lived two hundred years ago, I ________________

b If my parents had been movie stars, I ________________

c If I hadn't studied English, I ________________

d If I had been born in the United States, I ________________

VOCABULARY

1 **Underline the correct adverb.**

a **A**: Do you have any idea where you are going on vacation this year?
B: Yes, **clearly** / **hopefully** we're going to Tahiti.

b **A**: I bet you're feeling tired.
B: **Actually** / **Unfortunately**, I'm feeling fine.

c **A**: Have you heard any news about Helen recently?
B: Yes, Pete saw her last week. **Apparently** / **Personally**, she decided to quit her job.

d **A**: Did you get tickets for the Rolling Stones?
B: No. **Definitely** / **Predictably**, they sold out on the first day.

e **A**: Philip, what's wrong?
B: I don't know how to say this, but, **basically** / **surprisingly**, I don't want to see you anymore.

f **A**: So you hadn't seen her for twenty years?
B: That's right. But, **obviously** / **unbelievably**, she hadn't changed at all.

g **A**: Did you stay up late last night?
B: Yes. **Fortunately** / **Stupidly**, I didn't have go to work this morning.

2 **Complete the paragraph with appropriate adverbs from the list below.**

I'm (1) ________________ getting old. (2) ________________, I don't mind having less energy, but I'm very unhappy about the wrinkles. My face is (3) ________________ full of lines. (4) ________________ something had to be done, so I went shopping for anti-aging cream. I found a cream that promised to make me look ten years younger in a month. I (5) ________________ believed it and paid a lot of money. (6) ________________, I lost the instructions and I used the cream four times a day. (7) ________________, I was only meant to use it once a day. Now my face is bright red and the skin is peeling off. (8) ________________ my doctor will be able help me ... and I won't look ten years older!

1 fortunately / positively / definitely
2 Personally / Hopefully / Regularly
3 basically / stupidly / surprisingly
4 Predictably / Clearly / Actually
5 surprisingly / practically / stupidly
6 Fortunately / Unfortunately / Incredibly
7 Apparently / Naturally / Positively
8 Definitely / Honestly / Hopefully

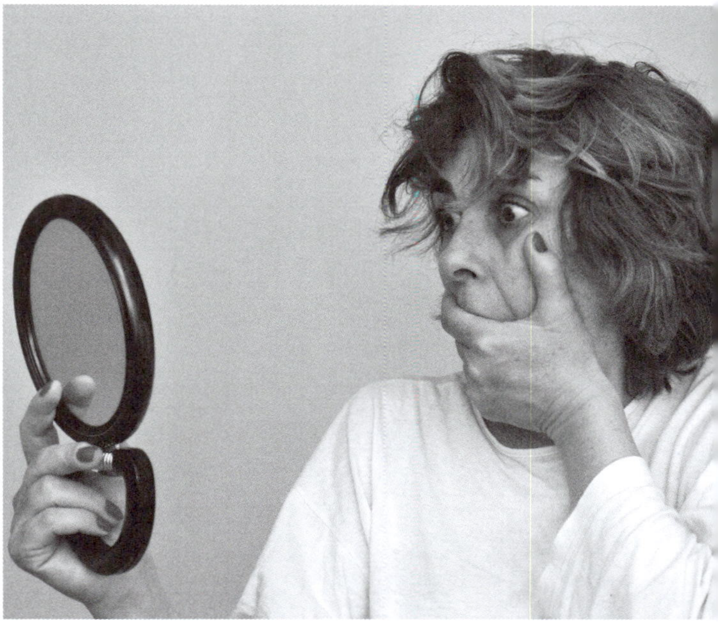

045 **Listen and check.**

3 **Write the words in order to make sentences.**

a a don't go I lot out .

I don't go out a lot.

b can't drive I well very .

c concerts don't enjoy going I much to very .

d childhood don't I my remember very well .

e a family I lot my see .

f I life live my sensibly very .

g abroad don't go I much very .

h I like loudly rock singing songs very .

Change the sentences to make them true for you.

4 **Put the telephone conversations into the correct order.**

a Hold on, please. I'll try to put you through ... I'm afraid he's on the other line. Would you like to hold? _____
Oh, hi. Is Tony there, please? _____
Hello. _____
Yes, thank you. _____

b Speaking. Who's calling, please? _____
Good morning. Clyde Interiors. Can I help you? _____
Hello. I'd like to speak to Don, please. _____
This is Miranda, from *Perfect Home* magazine. _____

c Tom, hold on. Can you call me back in five minutes? _____
Joanna? Hi, it's me. _____
Hi, Tom. Listen, I can't talk now. _____
Hello. _____
Just a quick question, OK? What are you doing later? _____

d Certainly. Are you available later on today? _____
Hello. My name is Mike Birdsell. _____
Hello. This is Eva Gomez. Can I help you? _____
Oh, yes, Mr. Birdsell. Thank you for getting back so quickly. We need to have a meeting. _____

046 **Listen and check.**

PRONUNCIATION

1 047 **Listen to two people speaking.**

Which speaker sounds more positive? Which speaker uses a higher tone of voice?

2 048 **Listen to the recording and practice saying the sentences in a positive way.**

a See you tomorrow then.
b I'll look forward to seeing you tomorrow.
c OK, I'll come over around seven.
d I see my family very regularly.
e I'm taking a training course next week.
f I've got something to tell you.

WRITING

Writing a story
Narrative organization

1 **Put the sentences in order to make the first part of a story.**

- a I had always wanted to be a photographer, but at first it was hard to find work.
- b It happened when I really wasn't expecting it.
- c Neither of those was the kind of work that I had dreamed of doing and I was afraid that it would continue like that forever.
- d Sometimes, I got jobs taking photographs for websites that sold electrical equipment.
- e Then, after two years, I got my first chance of a good picture.
- f To begin with, I made my living taking photographs at people's weddings.

1	2	3	4	5	6
a					

2 **Complete the second paragraph using the pictures and notes to help you. Begin like this:**
One day, I was downtown taking pictures ...

old man	running down the street
younger man	running after him
a gun	he looked
I thought	

I put out my foot — younger man — fell over

older man — ran away — not say anything

You may find the following expressions helpful.

> I knew I had to act fast.
> I knew I didn't have a second to lose.
> As quickly as I could, ...
> I was just about to ... when ...
> What happened next took me completely by surprise.

3 **Now write the final paragraph. Say what happened next to you, the young man, and the old man. Begin by completing the following sentence:**
If only I had stopped to think, ...

12 Style

GRAMMAR

1 **Insert the adjective in parentheses into the correct place in the sentence.**

a You would look great in a ^little black dress. (little)

b I can't believe he wears his old jeans to work! (blue)

c I love my leather purse. (Brazilian)

d How many patterned scarfs do you own? (silk)

e He always wears woolen sweaters. (enormous)

f I don't think you should wear an orange top with that long skirt. (purple)

g Not many people look good in shiny gold hot pants, but she does. (leopard-print)

2 **Decide where to put the words on the left in these descriptions of clothes.**

a snakeskin, old — a / an cowboy belt

____

b leather, black — a pair of motorcycle boots

____

c ridiculous, silk — a pair of baggy pants

____

d checked, large — a baseball cap

____

e cotton, brown — a / an old-fashioned shirt

____

f colorful, brand-new — a / an Italian tie

____

g long, plain black — a leather coat

____

3 **Complete the sentences using the structure *have something done*.**

a I didn't sharpen the knife myself. I *had it sharpened.*

b She doesn't wash her hair herself. She ____________________

c We didn't paint the house ourselves. We ____________________

d They didn't do all the work themselves. They ____________________ by a builder.

e She doesn't design the jewelry herself. She ____________________ by a professional.

f She doesn't color her hair herself. She ____________________ at the hairdresser.

g I haven't whitened my teeth myself. I ____________________ by a dentist.

4 **Read the sentences and underline the most appropriate verb form.**

a I need to **mend my coat / have my coat mended.** Do you know a good tailor?

b My husband **fixed the leak / had the leak fixed**. It took him hours.

c She's **making her wedding dress / having her wedding dress made** and the first fitting is today.

d I'm **cleaning the house / having the house cleaned** tomorrow. I just don't have time to do it myself.

e She **laid new tiles / had new tiles laid** in the kitchen. She did a great job!

f Let's **do our nails / have our nails done** together. We can go to my favorite nail salon.

g Can't you hear the phone ringing? You need to **test your ears / have your ears tested**.

5 Put the words in order to complete the question.

a cut do hair have you your
How often do you have your hair cut ________?

b ears ever had pierced you your
Have ________________________________?

c did eyes have last tested you your
When ________________________________?

d have home like redecorated to you your
Would ________________________________?

e a ever had Have of pair taken pants you
________________________________ up?

f do have you your repaired shoes
Where ________________________________?

g ever had Have picture taken you your
________________________________ by a professional photographer?

6 Write true answers to the questions in Exercise 5.

a ________________________________
b ________________________________
c ________________________________
d ________________________________
e ________________________________
f ________________________________
g ________________________________

VOCABULARY

1 Put the words in the box into the correct column.

~~baggy~~	~~belt~~	checked	~~cotton~~
dress	fur	jeans	leather
linen	long-sleeved	low-waisted	wool
pinstriped	plain	scruffy	shirt
silk	snakeskin	stylish	suede
suit	sweater	sweatshirt	top

Clothes	Materials	Adjective to describe clothes
belt	cotton	baggy

2 Look at the pictures and complete the texts with the words in the boxes.

a

Al

deep-set	freckles	mole	receding
sideburns	~~slim~~	streaks	wavy

Al is (1) slim and has dark, (2) ____________ hair with gray (3) ____________ and a (4) ____________ hairline. He has (5) ____________ eyes and long (6) ____________. He has (7) ____________ and a (8) ____________ on his chin.

b

Brad

bald	built	eyeliner	forehead
goatee	mustache	tattoo	

Brad is well (1) ____________ and has a (2) ____________ on his arm. He is (3) ____________ and has lines on his (4) ____________. He has a (5) ____________ beard and a (6) ____________. He wears black (7) ____________.

3 Underline the correct alternative.

On Sunday mornings, my husband always (1) **has** / **makes** me a cup of coffee and brings it to me in bed. I (2) **get** / **turn** the radio on and listen to the news before (3) **taking** / **making** a shower and (4) **doing** / **getting** dressed. I don't need to (5) **get** / **make** the children ready for school, so I have time to (6) **do** / **make** my t'ai chi exercises.

My husband likes to (7) **make** / **turn** the TV on and watch it while he's (8) **doing** / **having** a cup of coffee. After that, he does the housework, (9) **getting** / **making** the beds, (10) **doing** / **having** the dishes from the previous night, and so on.

4 Complete the text with the words in the box.

fits	get	go	look	look
match	put	~~try~~	wear	

I hate shopping for clothes. I don't need to (1) try ________ things on, because I know my size – only XXL (2) __________ me these days. I just want to get out of the store as quickly as possible. I always buy dark colors because bright ones don't (3) __________ good on me at all, and I always wear the same kinds of things. The only thing that matters is that I feel comfortable in what I (4) __________. In the mornings, I (5) __________ dressed very fast and (6) __________ on the first pair of jeans that I find. I always wear jeans because they (7) __________ with everything. I can't always find socks that (8) __________, but nobody sees them anyway.

I feel sorry for people who worry about what they (9) __________ like. There are more important things in life.

▶ 049 **Listen and check.**

5 Write the missing letters to complete the four mini-conversations.

A: That was very nice of you to give me that hat for my birthday. (1) T h a n k you.

B: You're (2) w _ _ _ _ _ e. My pleasure.

C: What a (3) b _ _ _ _ _ fu_ skirt! It really looks good on you.

D: Do you (4) t _ _ _ k so? Thank you.

E: Thank you so (7) m _ _ h for inviting us. We've had a wonderful few days.

F: Don't (8) m _ _ _ _ _ n it. I'm glad you could come.

G: What a fantastic dinner! That was absolutely (5) d _ _ _ _ _ _ _ s.

H: I'm (6) g _ _ d you enjoyed it. I know you like seafood.

PRONUNCIATION

1 ▶ 050 **Listen to the way the voice rises on each item in a list of words before falling at the end.**

He's in his early twenties ↗, tall ↗, dark ↗, good-looking ↗

and rich ↘.

2 ▶ 051 **Listen and repeat the sentences.**

a She's slim, elegant, good-looking, and married.
b He's smart, intelligent, attractive, and mine.
c She's got matching shoes, pants, hat, and bag.
d He's wearing a jacket, a belt, boots, jeans, and a T-shirt.

3 ▶ 052 **Listen to the lists below. Are they finished (the voice falls at the end) or unfinished (the voice rises at the end)?**

a We have it in a range of colors: blue and green, red and orange, black and white.
b They sell dresses, sweaters and tops, skirts, pants and jeans.
c Which style do you prefer: skinny, low-waisted, tight, or baggy?
d I have wavy hair, a mustache, sideburns, and a beard.

LISTENING

1 053 **Listen to a podcast about fashion designer Ralph Lauren. Check (✓) the main topic of the podcast.**

a his business sense

b his career

c his designs

2 Listen again. According to the show, are the statements true (T) or false (F)?

a Ralph Lauren has stores in different countries. T

b He has financial problems. ____

c He came from a very rich background. ____

d He began selling ties before he left school. ____

e He did not complete his education. ____

f He learned about fashion when he was in the army. ____

g He did not train as a fashion designer. ____

h Lauren's designs were highly fashionable and modern. ____

3 Find the phrases below in the listening script and check (✓) the best explanation.

a *a tale of rags to riches*
- ☐ a story about becoming wealthy
- ☐ a story about making money from clothes

b *he's never looked back*
- ☐ he has never looked at things twice
- ☐ he has become even more successful

c *that sets him apart*
- ☐ that was the reason for failing his exams
- ☐ that makes him special

d *he had a good eye*
- ☐ he did not need to wear glasses
- ☐ he had a natural talent for noticing

e *Lauren has it all*
- ☐ Lauren has everything that anyone could want
- ☐ Lauren is near the end of his life

Presenter: This week on *Catwalk Talk* we look at one of the biggest names in fashion, Ralph Lauren. Alison Martin, this is a big year for Ralph Lauren, isn't it?

Alison: Absolutely. This year marks the 50th anniversary of one of the most successful fashion houses ever. And Ralph Lauren certainly has good reason to celebrate. He has stores around the world, from Tokyo to Moscow to Milan, and his company is a multi-billion-dollar business.

Presenter: Ralph Lauren is a household name. He must be very rich.

Alison: His own personal wealth is estimated at five billion dollars and he has homes in New York, Colorado, and Jamaica. He also has world-famous collections of vintage automobiles and wristwatches.

Presenter: Was his family wealthy?

Alison: Absolutely not! Lauren's life story is a tale of rags to riches. He was born in New York, the son of immigrants from Belarus, his father a house painter, his mother a pianist.

Presenter: So how did it all begin?

Alison: In high school, he helped to make ends meet by selling ties to his classmates. He left college after two years – before completing his studies – and spent two years in the army. He then worked as a salesman before his career took off.

Presenter: And that was when he opened his first store? I read that he began by selling ties that he'd designed himself.

Alison: Yes, and after that he never looked back.

Presenter: How do you explain his incredible success?

Alison: During his years at college, Lauren studied business, not fashion, and it's this perhaps that set him apart from other fashion designers. There was nothing especially fashionable or modern about his designs, but he had a good eye for clothes, and an even better business sense.

Presenter: Lauren's most famous brands are, of course, Polo and Polo Sport, and his clothes are worn by everyone, from presidents to rappers and boxers.

Alison: Don't forget that Lauren doesn't only sell clothes; he sells a complete lifestyle. You can drink from Ralph Lauren glasses, eat from Lauren plates, and even sleep in Lauren sheets.

Presenter: Now in his seventies, Lauren has it all. He once said that he doesn't want to be too successful ... well, that kind of success would be fine with me!

Notes

Notes

Notes

Notes

Notes